Postman Pat™

ANNUAL 2000

Written by Brenda Apsley
Illustrated by Ray Mutimer
Designed by Julie Morris

POSTMAN PAT © Woodland Animations Limited 1999.
Licensed by Copyrights. All rights reserved.
Published in Great Britain in 1999 by
Egmont World Limited,
Deanway Technology Centre, Wilmslow Road,
Handforth, Cheshire SK9 3FB.
Printed in Italy
ISBN 0 7498 4288 1

£5.99
UK only

Contents

The Paper-chase

Early one morning, Postman Pat was just about to set off for the post office when Sara came downstairs waving a piece of paper.

"Don't forget the **shopping list**, Pat!" said Sara.

"I nearly did forget it," said Pat. "I'll put it in my pocket so I don't lose it. I'll do the shopping on the way home, but I'm going to help with the school paper-chase after work, so I might be a bit late."

"That's fine," said Sara. "See you later."

After a busy day at work, Pat met the Reverend Timms outside the school. He was helping with the paper-chase, too. The two of them tore up **lots** and **lots** of paper into small pieces. "I've brought lots of scrap paper from the post office," said Pat, pulling it out of his pockets.

Soon the children were ready in their shorts and T-shirts. "Off you go, Pat!" said the Reverend Timms.

6

Pat ran all around Greendale, leaving a trail of paper pieces behind him. He went past the church and along the high street. Then down to the duck pond and up to Granny Dryden's cottage. "It looks as if it's snowing!" she said when she saw all the pieces of white paper Pat was dropping.

Pat ran on past Garner Hall and as soon as he got back to the school, the children set off. They had to follow Pat's paper trail.

"See you soon!" said the Reverend Timms.

"Good luck," said Pat. "Don't forget to pick up all the paper scraps. Don't leave any litter in the village."

7

It wasn't long before the first runners got back. "Well done!" said Pat. He had a special certificate for each of them.

When the last runner had arrived, Pat put all the bits of paper in a carrier-bag. "I'll put these in the bin at home," he said.

When the children had all gone home, Pat drove his little red van to Sam Waldron's mobile shop to do the shopping.

"Hello, Pat," said Sam. "What can I get for you?"

Pat laughed. "I can't remember," he said. "But I've got a list."

Pat searched his pockets for the shopping list, but he couldn't find it. He searched them again. "Where can the shopping list be?" said Pat. "It must be here somewhere. I put it in my pocket this morning, **I know I did!**"

8

Pat searched his pockets again. And again. When he pulled out a little scrap of paper, he realised what had happened. **"Oh, no,"** he said. "I must have ripped up the shopping list and scattered it with the other paper-chase pieces!" He lifted up the carrier-bag of paper scraps to show Sam. "It's in here somewhere!"

A few minutes later, Julian passed Sam's mobile shop on his way home from school.

He was surprised to see his dad on his hands and knees trying to fit little bits of paper together. "What are you doing, Dad?" asked Julian.

"It's a long story, Julian," said Pat, trying to fit two pieces of paper together. He handed the carrier-bag to Julian. "Are you any good at doing jigsaw puzzles?" he asked.

9

A Jigsaw Picture

Poor Postman Pat! He had a lot of trouble trying to fit the torn-up pieces of shopping list together again.

Here is a jigsaw picture of Pat and Julian hard at work. Look at the jigsaw pieces that are left. Where do you think they will fit in the picture?

a b c d

3

4

Out in All Weathers

1. It is winter in Greendale. The weather is very cold, and an icy wind blows across the hills.

2. Lots and **lots** of snow falls in the night. It covers everything like a soft white blanket.

3. Pat gets up early to get ready for work. He looks out of the window and shivers. **"Brrr!"**

4. Pat has to deliver the post to the houses in Greendale in any kind of weather.

5. Pat knows how important it is for him to wear the right sort of warm clothes.

6. After eating a **big** bowl of warm porridge for breakfast, Pat gets ready for work.

7. Sara and Julian come downstairs in their pyjamas and dressing-gowns.

8. "We'll help you to collect all the **special** things you need today," says Sara.

9. Pat tells Sara and Julian what he needs. "First, my waterproof coat," says Pat.

10. "I need my waterproof trousers, too," says Pat. "And my wellington boots."

11. Julian finds the thick woolly scarf that Granny Dryden has knitted for Pat.

12. "Don't forget your gloves, Pat," says Sara. "The colours go with your uniform."

13. Sara makes a flask of warm tea for Pat to drink in the van.

14. There is even a soft, warm blanket for Jess the cat to sit on.

15. "Here's something else you need, Dad," says Julian. "My furry **ear-muffs**!"

16. Pat is about to go outside when he stops. "I need one more thing," he says.

17. Pat asks Julian to get two tennis rackets from the cupboard under the stairs.

18. Julian is puzzled. "This is the wrong time of year for playing tennis, Dad!" he says.

19. "I know!" laughs Pat. "But the tennis rackets will be very useful today, **I promise you**!"

Which Way?

Postman Pat delivers the post even in the snowiest weather.
He has some post for Peter Fogg.
There are two paths to Peter's cottage.
Which one will get Pat to the cottage in the quickest time?

Play the game with a friend.
You need a die and a counter each.
Play on one path each.
Take turns to roll the die.
Move along the path the number on the die.
If you score 2, move 2 spaces along the path, and so on.
The first player to get to Peter's cottage is the winner.

DANGER! BROKEN ICE

18

12
13
14
15
16
17
18
19
20

20
19
18
17
16
15
14
13
12
1

19

Sold, to Postman Pat!

Major Forbes decided that it would be nice if there were some seats on the grass near the village pond. "Lots of people enjoy going to feed the ducks," he said. "People will be able to sit down while they watch them."

Major Forbes decided to have a special sale called an auction to raise some money to buy the seats. "We all have things we don't want anymore," the major told Pat. "I'll sell unwanted things to whoever offers the most money for them."

"That's a really good idea of the Major's," said Pat. He was very pleased at the idea of getting rid of a very large, old pot that he and Sara didn't like at all. They had moved it out of the house, but it was taking up space in the garage.

"I'm going to give Major Forbes this old pot for his sale," Pat told Sara.

"But it's **horrible**!" said Sara. "Who will buy something like that?"

"Oh, someone will, I'm sure," said Pat.

Pat took Mrs Goggins to the sale in the village hall after they had finished work at the post office. Sara told Pat that she would come along later.

The sale started. Major Forbes held up the first thing to be sold. It was an awful painting of a big tree. Even the frame was broken. "Who will offer me fifty pence for this painting?" asked the major.

There was silence! No one said a word. No one raised a hand. Not one person wanted to buy the painting.

The major waited. "Come on now," he said. "Doesn't anyone like this painting?"

It was very hot in the village hall, so Pat put his hand up to take his cap off.

When the major saw him, he smiled and pointed to Pat. "Thank you, Pat," he said. "The painting is sold to Postman Pat!"

"Oh, no!" Pat whispered to Mrs Goggins. "I've bought that **awful** painting! What will Sara say?"

The sale went very well. Mrs Pottage bought a desk for the twins, and Mrs Goggins bought a shawl that Granny Dryden had knitted. Ted Glen bought some old tools, and PC Selby bought a bell for his bike.

The major was enjoying himself. "What will you give me for this fine ... er ... statue?" he said. Ted had made it out of old bits of wood and scrap metal.

"Look at the size of that thing!" said Pat. "It's **enormous**! What a mess!"

"What time is it, Pat?" whispered Mrs Goggins.

It was four o'clock. Pat didn't want to make a noise, so he held up four fingers.

"Four pounds!" said Major Forbes.

"That is very generous. Sold to Postman Pat for four pounds!"

24

Soon it was time for Pat's old pot to be sold. He watched as a few people made bids for it, then he saw Sara in the doorway. "Over here, Sara!" he said, waving his hand to attract her attention.

Major Forbes saw him, and thought he wanted to buy the pot! "Sold to Postman Pat!" he said.

"Oh, no!" said Pat. "Now I've bought that big old pot back!"

When Pat and Sara got home after the auction, Julian was waiting in the garden. He couldn't wait to see what they had bought. "Did you buy some nice things?" he asked.

"Don't ask!" said Pat, as he tried to force the garage door closed. "I've got even **more** rubbish than I started with!"

Read with Postman Pat

Can you read this story with Postman Pat? The little pictures will help you.

Major Forbes wanted to put some

near the  . People could

sit down to watch the  .

 had a sale in the village hall.

Mrs Pottage bought a  .

"It's for  ," she said.

Peter Fogg bought a  .

 bought a green  .

26

"That  will fit on my  ,"

said Miss Hubbard.

"What did you buy at the sale, Dad?"

asked  . "A new

for  ? Or a silver  ?

Pat didn't want to show Julian what

was in the  !

Can you guess why?

Yes,  had bought a load of

old rubbish!

Charlie's New Shoes

I. Charlie's **big** black shoes are worn out. There are **big** holes in the toes.

2. Charlie goes to Trader Jones's store to get a new pair. "Colour, black," he says. "Size, **extra** large."

3. Trader looks in boxes, on shelves, and in cupboards. At last, he finds some shoes.

4. "The shoes are all right. But I like my shoes much bigger, and a lot longer," says Charlie.

5. The shoes are all Trader has, so Charlie takes them home. He leaves them outside his caravan.

6. Charlie goes to find a rolling-pin. "If I hit the shoes, it will make them **flatter** and **longer**," he says.

7. Arnold arrives and sits down to wait for Charlie. He sits on the shoes and squashes them flat!

8. "You're sitting on my new shoes," says Charlie. Arnold jumps. "Oh, sorry, Charlie," he says.

9. But Charlie is pleased. "Look, my shoes are much **longer** now," he says. "Good old Arnold!"

10. Charlie goes off to get some shoe polish. He leaves his new shoes outside the caravan.

11. Edward comes to visit Charlie. He sits down to wait for Charlie to come home.

12. Edward gets tired of waiting. He yawns – and falls fast asleep on Charlie's new shoes!

13. When Charlie gets back he shakes Edward to wake him. "You are lying on my shoes," he says.

14. Edward jumps up. The shoes are very **long**, and very **flat**. "Oh!" says Edward. "Sorry, Charlie."

15. But Charlie is pleased. Now his new shoes are just the same size as his old ones. **"Perfect!"** says Charlie.

Dot•to•Dot
with Charlie Chalk

Join the dots to finish Charlie Chalk in his new shoes.
Then you can colour him in.

Bubbles

Postman Pat was cleaning his little red van outside the post office one afternoon when the Reverend Timms came along. "Hello, Vicar," said Pat. "Is something wrong? You look worried."

"It's the village hall," said the vicar. "It needs a new coat of paint, but there's no money to pay for it."

"Why not have a jumble sale?" said Pat.

"We had one in spring," said the Reverend Timms. "We need a new idea."

Pat squeezed out his soapy sponge. "I know," he said. "We'll clean cars on Saturday morning. We'll use the money we collect to buy some paint."

"That's a **great idea**, Pat!" said the vicar. "I'll go and ask Sam and Ted and the others to help. See you on Saturday!"

33

The Reverend Timms was the first to arrive at the village hall. He lined up lots of **big** buckets of water so there would be one for each helper.

Sara was the next to arrive. She squirted some soapy liquid into each bucket, then went into the hall to find some rubber gloves to wear.

Miss Hubbard was next. She squirted some soapy liquid into the buckets, then she went off to park her bike.

When Ted Glen arrived there were no cars waiting, so he went into the hall to have a cup of tea. On his way he squirted some soapy liquid into the buckets.

Sam Waldron arrived in his mobile shop. "Come and have a cup of tea!" called Ted, and Sam went off into the hall — but not before he added some soapy liquid to each bucket.

Postman Pat was the last helper to arrive. His van had got very dirty since he last cleaned it, so he decided to start washing it as the others came out of the hall. He picked up a **big** sponge – and squirted lots of soapy liquid into each of the buckets.

As Pat started work, Doctor Gilbertson and Mrs Pottage arrived to have their cars cleaned. Peter Fogg brought his big red tractor!

Pat's van was soon covered in lots and lots of foamy bubbles – and so was Pat. There were **bubbles everywhere**! Jess had fun chasing the ones that floated into the air, popping them on the end of his nose.

There were so many bubbles on Doctor Gilbertson's car that she could hardly see it.

"My tractor looks as if it's covered in whipped cream!" said Peter.

Clouds of soapy, shiny white bubbles floated around. The wind blew them all over Greendale.

The helpers rinsed and rinsed the cars, but they just **couldn't** get rid of the bubbles!

"I didn't put a lot of soapy liquid in the water," said Sara.

"Neither did I," said Miss Hubbard.

"And I only added one squeeze," said Ted.

"I added two squirts," said Pat. "But they were only little ones."

The Reverend Timms laughed. "I know why there are so many bubbles," he said. "You **all** put soapy liquid in the water. And I had put it in already!"

Just then, PC Selby arrived on his bike. "Now then," he said. "Who is responsible for covering Greendale in bubbles?"

He laughed when he heard about the mix-up. "This is very serious," he said with a big smile. "But I'll let you all off – as long as you give my bike a good wash!"

Pop Go the Bubbles

There were bubbles everywhere when Pat and the others were washing cars outside the village hall. Jess had a lot of fun trying to pop them.

Play the bubbles game with a friend.
You need a coin and 20 counters each (or you can use buttons).

Choose a row of bubbles to play on.
Take turns to flip the coin. If the coin lands head-up, pop one bubble by covering it with a counter or button. If the coin lands tail-up, pop two bubbles by covering them.
The first to pop all his or her bubbles wins the game.

You can play the game on your own, too. How many turns does it take to pop all the bubbles?

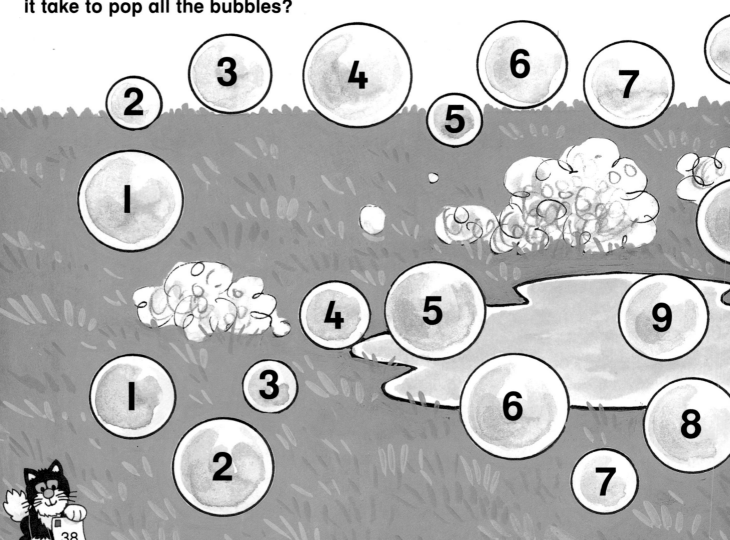

Long Ago in Greendale

There was a special party in Greendale. It was to celebrate the first day of the new year, the year 2000.

"I wonder what living in Greendale used to be like long ago?" asked Julian.

Pat helped him to find out ...

A **very** long time ago, before we started counting in years, people lived in groups. They moved around from place to place, hunting animals for food. They wore animal skins to keep warm, and learned how to make fire and cook meat.

People slept outdoors, or in caves until they learned how to build shelters like tents. They used animal skins, bones, tree branches and stones.

When they learned how to catch and keep wild animals they stayed in one place. They used animals such as cows, sheep and oxen for meat, milk, skins and wool. Walls and fences stopped the animals running away.

People used to collect wild foods such as berries and nuts. They learned how to grow crops – wheat, corn and barley – and used them to make bread. These people, the first farmers, soon learned how to use oxen and horses to help them.

Because farmers stayed in one place, they built houses. These were small huts made of mud and straw, with a hole for a door. People and their animals lived inside!

Postman Pat's New Hobby

1. Postman Pat is looking at the notice-board outside the village hall one day.

2. The cards and papers on the notice-board tell people what is going on in Greendale.

3. Along comes the Reverend Timms. "Are you looking for a new hobby, Pat?" he asks.

4. "Hello, Reverend," says Pat. "Yes, I like trying new things, don't you? It's **good fun**."

5. "There are lots of things to choose from," says the vicar. "Keep-fit class on Mondays."

6. "Granny Dryden is showing people how to bake cakes on Tuesday afternoons," says Pat.

7. "There's the singing group on Wednesday, and a flower-arranging class on Thursday."

8. "What about joining my bell-ringing class on Fridays?" says the Reverend Timms.

9. "Or I could join Ted Glen's car maintenance class on Saturday mornings," says Pat.

10. Pat can't decide what to try until he sees a small card. It says **Pottery for beginners**.

11. "I have **always** wanted to try pottery," says Pat. "I bet Miss Hubbard is a good teacher."

12. Pat tells Sara that he is going to try a new hobby, but he doesn't tell her what it is.

13. "I will give you the first thing I make as a gift," Pat tells Sara. "It will be a surprise."

14. At Pat's first lesson, Miss Hubbard makes a lovely vase. "Your turn now, Pat," she says.

15. Pat sits at the potter's wheel. He has a **big** lump of clay, and shapes it with wet hands.

16. He pushes a pedal to turn the wheel. But it turns a **lot** faster than Pat expects it to!

17. The clay is very soft – and very slippery. It keeps slipping out of Pat's wet hands.

18. Bits of wet clay fly everywhere. They cover Pat, his clothes – and even poor Miss Hubbard!

19. Pat's pot is a very odd shape! It has lumps and bumps, and leans over to one side.

20. At the next class Pat fires his pot in the kiln until it is hard and takes it home to give to Sara.

21. Sara takes the pot out of its box. She holds it sideways, upside down, and even back-to-front.

22. "Thank you, Pat," she says. "It's ... er ... lovely. Very ... er ... unusual. But what is it?"

23. Pat laughs as Jess puts his head right inside the pot. "That's the mystery!" he says. **"I don't know!"**

Read with Postman Pat

Read this story yourself. The little pictures will help you.

The village hall in Greendale is a very

busy place. There is a

class on Monday. On Tuesday

shows how to make

There is a class on

Wednesday, and lessons

on Thursday.

48

shows how to ring

on Friday. On Saturday has a

class.

tries the pottery class with .

He makes a pot for .

"What can I do with this?" asks Sara.

looks inside to find out!

49

Frogs Crossing!

Postman Pat had a very busy morning. He got back to the post office much later than usual.

"You're late today," said Mrs Goggins, looking at the **big** clock behind the counter. "Did you have trouble with the van?"

Pat shook his head. "No, the van is fine," said Pat. "It was the frogs that made me late."

"Frogs!" said Mrs Goggins. "Whatever do you mean, Pat? How can frogs make you late?"

Pat explained. "All the roads around the village pond were busy," he said. "But not with cars and vans. They were covered in frogs. The frogs are all making their way to the pond to lay their eggs."

"Well, I never!" said Mrs Goggins.

"Frogs don't hop very fast," Pat said. "Every time I had to drive near the pond I had to stop the van and wait until they all got across the road safely."

50

Julian and his friend Charlie Pringle saw the frogs on their way home from school.

That night, Pat told Julian why the frogs were hopping to the pond. "They go back there every year to lay their eggs," he said. "The eggs grow into little tadpoles, then into frogs."

"I hope the frogs don't get run over," said Julian. "Some of them are so small that drivers might not see them."

Pat was worried about the frogs, too. It wasn't safe for them to cross the busy road. "I don't mind stopping the van and waiting for them to cross the road," he said. "I know they are there. But other drivers might not see them."

"We have a special crossing outside school so that we can cross the road safely," said Julian. "The signs say **TAKE CARE – CHILDREN CROSSING**. That's what the frogs need – a special place to cross!"

Pat laughed. "You know, that's not as silly as it sounds, Julian!" he said. "In fact, it's a good idea. A very good idea!"

After supper that night, Pat got busy in his shed. He was in there until it got dark. Sara and Julian didn't know what he was doing, but they heard lots of sawing and hammering sounds. Pat was still in his shed when Julian went up to bed.

In the morning, Pat left for work before Julian got up, but he saw his dad on his way to school.

There, near the pond, Julian found out just what his dad had been up to in his shed. Pat had made some signs to warn drivers that there were frogs crossing the road. **TAKE CARE**, the signs said. **FROGS CROSSING!**

FROGS CROSSING!

PC Selby held up his hand to stop the traffic as the frogs hopped across the road.

"So that's what you were up to, Dad!" said Julian. "Making special signs for the frogs."

"Yes," said Pat. "And they were your good idea, Julian. Now, off you go to school. I'm not sure your teacher will believe you if you tell her it was the frogs that made you late!"

SAMI

Count with Postman Pat

There are lots of frogs on their way to the pond. They can hop across the road safely thanks to special signs Pat made. Now everyone in Greendale knows they are there, and can take extra care.

There are frogs everywhere!
Look carefully – how many can you count in the picture?

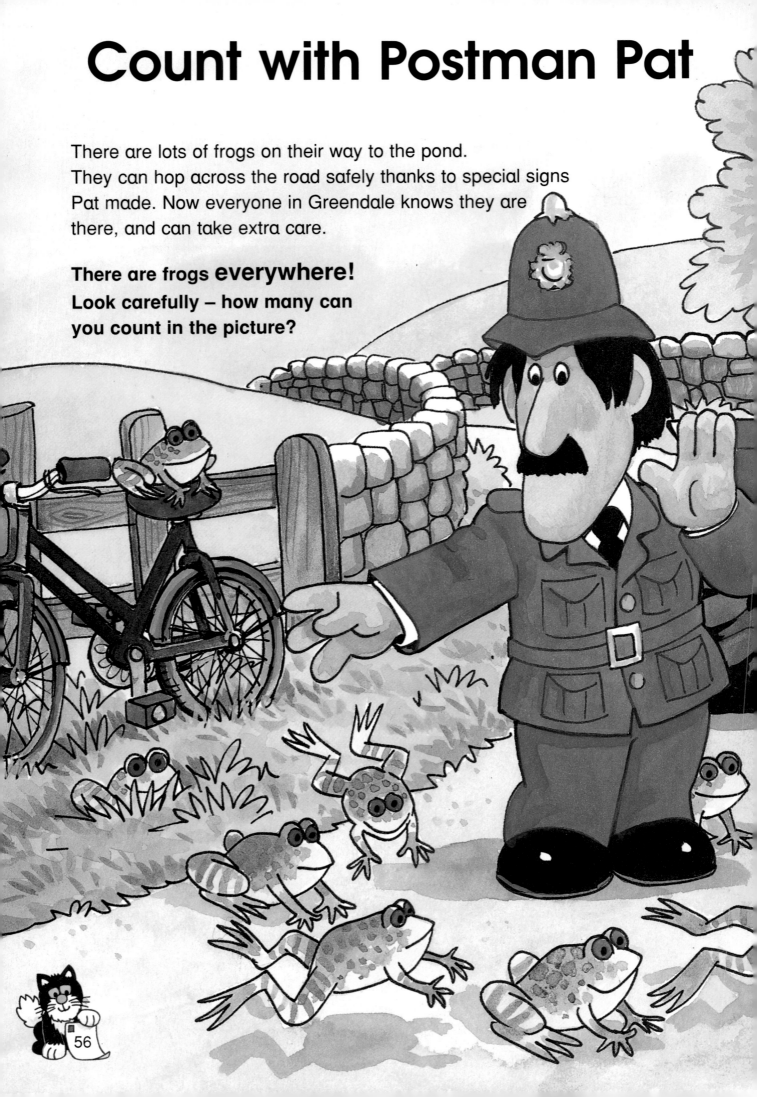

57

Paint Pots

I. Trader Jones is **very** busy. Charlie and his friends want to make the island neat and tidy.

2. They go to Trader's store for tins of paint. "Yellow for me," says Charlie. "It's for my caravan door."

3. "I want red paint," says Captain Mildred. "Because A, I like it, and B, it's the colour of Buttercup's funnel."

4. "The doors of my store need painting," says Trader. "But I'm too busy finding paint for you lot."

5. "I'll paint them for you," says Arnold. "And I'll help," says Edward. "I like painting."

6. Trader finds the tins of paint, but there's a **problem** – the labels have all come off.

7. Trader doesn't know which label goes with which tin. "I'll have to guess which is which," he says.

8. Trader gives tins of paint to Charlie and Captain Mildred. He hopes they are the right colours.

9. "Where is our paint?" asks Arnold. Trader is fed up. "Take as many tins as you like," he says.

10. Captain Mildred is soon back at Trader's store. "I do NOT like Buttercup's pink funnel!" she says.

11. Charlie comes back, too. "My caravan looks really silly with an orange door," he says.

12. Trader remembers that he let Edward and Arnold use **any** tins of paint they wanted to.

13. "Oh, no!" says Trader. "I wonder what Arnold and Edward have done to my doors!"

"Join my club!"

Postman Pat™ GREENDALE CLUB POST OFFICE

I know just how much children love receiving parcels and letters so, when *you* join the Postman Pat Club, I've arranged to send you up to nine different deliveries!

- **Fantastic Welcome Pack**
  A great pack full of Postman Pat goodies.

- **Birthday card**
  from Pat and Jess.

- **Christmas card**
  and news from Greendale.

- **Six character cards**
  These can be coloured in and sent to Greendale, and each character will send you back a colour postcard with message to stick on your poster.*

For the Welcome Pack alone you might expect to pay at least £13 if you could get it in the shops, but annual membership, including birthday and Christmas cards is just **£9.99** (+ 73p postage).

With a 14 day no quibble money-back guarantee!

How to enrol

Return the coupon right (or a photocopy) to:
Postman Pat Club, Valley of Greendale, PO Box 142, Horsham RH13 5FJ.
Credit card orders may call 01403 242727 or fax 01403 261555.

Please Note: Exact contents of the Welcome Pack may change from time to time. Allow 28 days for delivery. After 30/12/00 please call to check the price. All communications (except the Welcome Pack) will be via parents/guardians.
*SAE required. Promoter: Robell Media Promotions Limited, registered in England number. 2826424. POSTMAN PAT™ © Woodland Animations Ltd 1999. Licensed by Copyrights.

Great Prize Draw

Win one of 10 fabulous Postman Pat Activity Centres

10 lucky winners will be drawn at random to each receive a fabulous Postman Pat Post Office. A safe, store-room, envelopes and stamps, mobile phone, play money, parcels and play food provide hours of fun. There's even Granny Dryden's pension book & Ted Glen's savings book. Excellent! And don't worry, if you are not a winner, the playset is available from most good toy retailers.

Everyone who is a Postman Pat Club member on the 14/1/2000 will be automatically entered into the draw so if you have not joined, don't delay, sign up today.

Rules:
1. 10 winners will be chosen at random and will be notified by post.
2. No purchase necessary. To enter without enrolling in The Postman Pat Club, send child's name, age and address and parents name on a postcard marked "PP2000 Draw" to , PO Box 142, Horsham, RH13 5FJ. Entries limited to one per person. Closing date 14/1/2000.
3. No correspondence will be entered in to.
4. A list of winners will be made available on request from Robell Media Promotions Ltd, PO Box 142, Horsham,RH13 5FJ after 14/2/2000. S.A.E. required.
5. Prize content may be varied subject to availability.

Robell Club

Please ensure the coupon is filled in by an adult.

Please enrol the following in The Postman Pat Club at £10.72 (inc postage).
Member's Full Name : _____ Address:_____
_____
_____ Post Code:_____ Date of birth:____/____/
Your Name:_____ Address (if different):_____
_____ Post Code:_____
Name of child's parent or guardian (if not you):_____
❑ Please enter me in the prize draw
❑ I enclose a cheque or postal order for £10.72 payable to Postman Pat Club
❑ Please charge the sum of £10.72 to my MasterCard (Access) / Visa account
Card number: ⬚⬚⬚⬚ ⬚⬚⬚⬚ ⬚⬚⬚⬚ ⬚⬚⬚⬚   Expiry: _____/

Data Protection Act: If you do **not** wish to receive other offers from us or companies we recommend, please tick this box ❑